Nicolas and the Six Bells

The Reverend David Ackerman

Illustrated by Helena Tarrant

With a foreword by The Dean of Windsor

DA PUBLISHING
London, UK

⇒●⇐

This book is dedicated to

My family and parishioners, especially Andrea my mother and
my aunt Louise, for whom better days returned.

Tony Fernandes, CBE

⇒●⇐

ACKNOWLEDGEMENTS

Those in Kensal Green who throughout Lent and Easter 2020 increased the power of
the weak and demonstrated, in the words of Her Majesty The Queen, "The attributes
of self-discipline, good-humoured resolve and fellow-feeling which still characterise
this country", including local shopkeepers, Jessie and the staff at Parlour, Kensal refuse
collectors, delivery drivers, postmen, community volunteers and
Bona the window cleaner.

The Hon Karen Buck MP, Dr Maurice Merrell FISOB, Cllr Patricia Mcalliser,
Anne Abel BEM, Yvonne Jarman, Ryan Dalton, Janine Ryan, Riccardo Moore,
Stella Wilson, Fr Gary Bradley, Valerie Vamanrav, Richard Ward, Georgina Graham,
Fr Paul Thomas and Tracy Brent.

Bernadette Barrett and Sarah Chipchase.

The Revd Ken Jacques, minister at Harting Congregational Church, Sussex.

Simon Adams and all who cast the bells at the John Taylor Bell Foundry.

First published in 2020 in the United Kingdom by
DA PUBLISHING
Kensal Green, Middlesex, England

ISBN 978-1-5272-6377-2

Cover illustration by Helena Tarrant / Cover design by Nick Snode

Typeset in Cronos Pro 14pt/16pt and Frambuesa Black 22pt
Printed on 150gsm Magno Satin (silk)
Printed and bound by Whitehall Printing, Bristol, UK
www.whitehallprinting.co.uk

This book is printed in the UK on FSC certified paper, using fully
sustainable vegetable-oil based inks.

Book production by

GABRIEL BOOKS
www.gabrielbooks.co.uk
gabriel.bks@btinternet.com

Contents

Foreword

SIX NEW BELLS for St John's Church, Kensal Green, the anticipation of celebrations on the 75th anniversary of V E Day, and then the unexpected lockdown because of the Covid-19 pandemic (during which the bells continued to ring) – these events and experiences clearly made David Ackerman think seriously and deeply about the values, beliefs and memories that he wishes to be cherished and preserved. So, during what was possibly the most challenging period of his ministry so far, he decided to work on and complete his children's story: *Nicolas and the Six Bells*.

This delightful story, charmingly illustrated by Helena Tarrant, is a tale of exile and return; loss and re-discovery. It is both a warning and a celebration. It reminds us of just how carelessly we can turn our backs on the wisdom we have learnt down through the ages. At the same time, it invites us to believe that wisdom is never entirely lost; it will endure. Somewhere, deep in our human consciousness, it is as if a bell will ring and we shall recognise what will bring us true contentment.

Though the outline of the story is very simple, as it unfolds we come across a number of allusions, historical and religious. This need not worry us. As the author writes when commenting on a question asked by the young boy Gabriel, asking questions is "something children are good at". This little book invites its readers to explore and enquire along the way.

Nevertheless, *Nicolas and the Six Bells* remains an enchantingly innocent narrative for children. No doubt, we adults will enjoy our sophisticated interpretation of the story. At the same time however, we might envy those young people who are able to enter into it through the gift of the imagination, 'feel' the truth of it, and be nourished by it. I hope and pray that those young people will be many.

To David Ackerman and to 'Aid to the Church in Need', I give my thanks, and pray that the bells, both literally and metaphorically, will go on ringing.

David Conner
DEAN OF WINDSOR

Introduction

IN THIS STORY a brother and sister go on an adventure to find something they are not supposed to discover. We can begin a journey and on the way discover something we never knew existed, often within ourselves. Life and faith are both types of journeys, and their beginnings and endings have inspired numerous stories, not least this one. I could not have imagined I would complete this book sitting in a field in Sussex.

When did the story of *Nicolas and the Six Bells* begin to be written? I have no idea. It might be something you can work out. Neither do I know how this story will end, that I suppose depends on each reader's response.

This story, which was originally written as a play about six new church bells, was always going to make reference to the seventy fifth anniversary of the ending of the Second World War in Europe. Who would have imagined, late in 2019, how important the themes in this story would become.
As I look out over Sussex, far away in Russia people were celebrating the great Festival of Easter. A work about bells, based on what happened to the Church in Russia during the years of Communism, had turned into a profound meditation on freedom itself. For much of the life of the Soviet Union, churches were not closed for a time for people's safety but to stop people believing in God.

You might notice in this story references to the *Chronicles of Narnia*, which I loved to read as a child. Many new stories re-tell in new ways what has been told before, this is another.

In C.S. Lewis' *The Lion, the Witch and the Wardrobe* four children enter a land where it is always winter and never Christmas. What struck me only recently is that the chronicles are at heart a story about how brothers and sisters, sent away from their families for their safety during the Second World War, became saints.

I hope this book might help in a small way to inspire you to seek out the great people of the past. Many can inspire you, especially the saints. Be courageous, be brave, one day be leaders of a more just and equal society.
It is never too late to change and it is never too late to learn. Make the words of Nicolas at the end of this book (first spoken by Sir Winston Churchill and Martin Luther King) your own:

> This is your hour
> work together,
> pray together,
> struggle together,
> stand up for freedom together,
> let freedom ring."

Do that and one day you will be a saint yourself.

David Ackerman,
West Marden, Sussex April 2020

ONE
A very unhappy country

ONCE UPON A TIME, not very far away, and not very long ago, there was a country called Ophis.

It was a very unhappy country because people were not allowed to have parties. Children never celebrated birthdays or lay in bed on Christmas Eve looking forward to getting up and opening presents.

In this country Christmas was never celebrated, another of the many reasons everyone was so unhappy. When the winds changed and winter came no one looked forward to the night Father Christmas would visit, and parties raise people's spirits on dark evenings. In fact there was nothing to look forward to at all. The only party allowed was in one place on New Year's Eve, with a few boring fireworks. But why celebrate a new year, when it would be like the last?

This country hadn't always been unhappy. Its people were once famous for dancing and singing and its hills and mountains echoed with the sound of bells. Then everything changed and life became very quiet, very boring and each day like the next.

If you were lucky your mother or father would tell you stories about the 'old days', but that made them sad too! But most sad of all, in this saddest of countries, was that when winter came there was never Christmas.

The changing of the Guard

To know why this had come about we must start at the ending of something very special and be introduced to someone very odd. Ophis was in fact a new name for this Island without parties.

The country had until quite recently been called Kolokol, but the name was changed when Ophis Kirtle became its leader. Ophis is a strange name for a country, and a man, and he was a strange man indeed. He always wore the same green clothes, in summer and winter, and was very tall. He wore thin pointy shoes that curled at the end, and on his head his hair would stick up in the shape of a 'V'.

He looked uncommonly like a snake. Unlike a snake however he was very particular about what he ate. If he came to dinner you had to prepare a gluten and nut free vegan meal, although thankfully he was quite content eating a raw carrot. Ophis loved carrots. He may have had odd tastes and looked strange but he was intelligent and cunning. There is a saying, never judge a book by its cover, and because people would laugh at him they didn't see the danger lurking beneath the laughter.

Every morning as his long legs moved his thin body out of bed, in his cold bedroom, he would say to himself, "Better to be feared than to be loved". Ophis had never, from an early age, enjoyed parties because he didn't make friends easily and became so used to being unhappy himself he couldn't see the point of them. Ophis was feared but he feared little. One thing came close however: the sound of bells. Why he feared the ringing of bells is a story that needs telling first. It begins when the happy Kingdom of Kolokol was alive with parties to welcome its new King. Ophis' fear came from what

Nicolas, the last of the bishops, said to him. Then the King had to leave, and slowly – like a great big dark cloud on a sunny day – unhappiness descended.

For many years Ophis had worked for King Edmund. His job was to raise money in taxes (he was called the Chancellor) and he was always thinking of new ways to make money. He wanted to tax sugar and cakes – his party tax – but King Edmund always laughed when his sugar hating sour faced chancellor made silly suggestions. Ophis found politicians much happier to follow his advice. As the years went by Ophis grew more and more angry and unhappy (which are the same thing really) and – like such people – he began to envy other people's happiness.

King Edmund grew in wisdom but also in age (they often go together too!) and one day, watching the guard change outside the palace, he decided to ask to see Bishop Nicolas. Ophis hated Bishop Nicolas because not only was he happy, he had the gift of making others happy too. He also clearly liked cakes.

He was generous to people who needed help and would leave gifts without people knowing who had paid for them.

The reason for their meeting was that Prince John, who would be the next King, was only two years old.

When Kings are very young they need someone to work with them and make decisions for them. If another country was to start a war a two year old isn't really able to decide what to do! The person who speaks for a young (or very sick or old) king is called a regent. In London a famous park is named after the son of a King who did this job.

Kolokol needed a Regent. King Edmund knew that the one person who could never do the job was tall, thin, wore green clothes and ate carrots for breakfast. The one person who could be was good and generous and well loved. So he decided to ask Bishop Nicolas.

"I asked to see you today because, watching the guard change, a tune came into my head", said the old King to Nicolas, "there is a song about two children visiting a palace and they look through the railings and watch as some guards arrive to replace the guards who need a rest. They wonder what it's like to guard the palace and live in it and Alice says to Christopher Robin, 'I wouldn't be King for a hundred pounds' ".

As Nicolas sipped his tea he could see tears in the King's old eyes and through them the King read the last line of the song from a small book:

> They're changing guard at Buckingham Palace –
> Christopher Robin went down with Alice.
> "Do you think the King knows all about me?"
> "Sure to, dear, but it's time for tea," says Alice.

"To be a great leader is to love your people, but also to know them. Little Prince John only knows about toys, and asking Alexa to play songs, and he sees the world as a great place to play in. You know the people, and you love them. Take care of him and when I meet in another country, probably very soon, the King I have tried to serve all my life I hope I can say that I have done my best, done my duty to God, helped others, and know that one day we will meet again".

After giving the King a blessing Nicolas stood up and, as things were done properly in Kolokol, he left the room walking backwards. As he turned to bow (grateful he hadn't fallen over a toy) he knew that he wouldn't see good King Edmund again.

TWO
A Bell and a Ring

ONE SLATE GREY FROSTY MORNING when everything was silent and the birds had not yet awoken, the great bell of Myra Cathedral began to ring. Myra was the capital city of Kolokol and many had never heard the great bell toll. Older people, waking to the sad tolling of the bell, knew that the old King had died. Meanwhile in the Palace John slept in his cot, hugging Humpty Dumpty. Quietly the nursery door was opened and two people entered and knelt.

Princess Frederica was John's great aunt and with her was Nicolas. He took John's little hand and kissed it and placed on his finger a gold ring. This was the signet ring of Kolokol and no law could ever be made without this ring being used. This was the protection the King good give, without his seal, no bad law could pass.

Nicolas then took the ring and placed it on his finger as Regent and asked God to bless the little boy who became king in his sleep lying next to Humpty.

After King John had been washed and dressed, Nicolas and the Princess carried him to the balcony of the Palace, and with John they stepped outside to the ringing of the palace bells, the salute of bands and the cheers of the crowd.

"You will be a great King", whispered Nicolas, and as they waved he thought of his friend King Edmund and how odd life can be: how happiness and sadness can exist at the same time, if combined with hope.

Ophis, who had been woken up by the sound of the bell, smiled through his thin lips. He knew that he would not be Regent and that Nicolas would soon find a new Chancellor. Chewing on his carrot he decided to act. For many years he knew that if he could not be close to power he would take it for himself. Being cunning, he knew that the moment a crown passes to a new king it can be an uncertain time for the country and the best way of turning people against someone or something popular is to tell a lie. Tell it quickly and often and it soon does its work. Ophis left the Palace in a flash of green and went to the television studio.

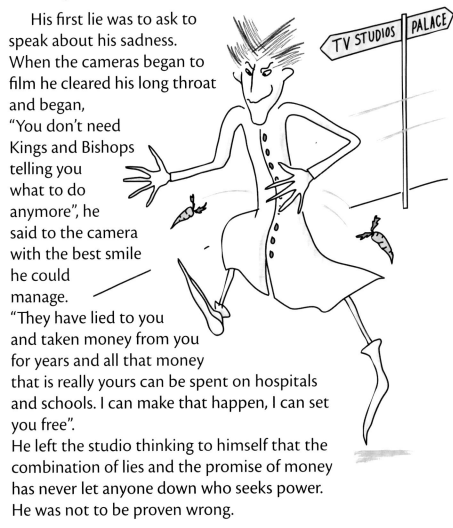

His first lie was to ask to speak about his sadness. When the cameras began to film he cleared his long throat and began,
"You don't need Kings and Bishops telling you what to do anymore", he said to the camera with the best smile he could manage.
"They have lied to you and taken money from you for years and all that money that is really yours can be spent on hospitals and schools. I can make that happen, I can set you free".
He left the studio thinking to himself that the combination of lies and the promise of money has never let anyone down who seeks power.
He was not to be proven wrong.

It was just before Christmas when Nicolas went to the Palace, passing a crowd shouting, "Ophis, Ophis".
His lies had done their trick.

The Bishop found Princess Frederica, collected John and Humpty Dumpty, and Nicolas said the time had come for them to leave:

"It is only when we lose something precious that we realise what it meant to us. Wherever we go all that is good in this Kingdom will be with us and live, and one day we will return. Many have had to leave their homes and lands and find somewhere to live and believe in freedom. Once a small boy was taken to Egypt because a ruler feared the message he would bring. But he will be with us too".

Nicolas handed John, with Humpty, to the Princess and put into a large leather bag the crown (which had been too big for John at his coronation) and three small bags of money to pay for their journey.
They found Rigsby the palace cat (Ophis hated cats) and set out on their journey. They would head for the mountains, find people to give them shelter and food, and in a boat sail across the sea.

They would land on one of the lone Islands, whose people lived under the Crown of Kolokol, and amongst whom their little King would grow up.

THREE
We will be with our friends again

THAT NIGHT they stayed in a small cottage where a friend of the bishop had given them shelter. The following morning Nicolas asked for a pen, some paper, and hurriedly wrote a letter. This is what he wrote:

To Ophis Kirtle

When the people believed they no longer wanted a King you persuaded them to decide what they are against. They do not yet know what they are for. Your power rests on lies and you will only keep power by telling more. When everyone knows that they are no longer free to believe or decide anything, the only thing that will unite them is fear. You once said to me that when you have ended the days of Kings and Bishops you will silence a sound that reminds people of them. The bells of Kolokol. Bells said goodbye to a King and their sound welcomed a new one. When we were at war their silence spoke of hope of victory. They are the sound and noise of freedom. They are a song of faith; the tune of happiness and loss, joy and grief, thanksgiving and desire. A great sadness will come upon this land when that sound is no longer heard, but for as long as one person remembers what a bell sounds like there is hope. You may take away all the bells of Kolokol but I promise you that one day a bell will be found. On the day it is rung your rule will end. Freedom will return and so shall I.
We will meet again, I promise.

Nicolas.

Nicolas folded the letter and everyone gathered their belongings in preparation for the journey. The friend set off with the letter having been told whom he could trust, and that afternoon it was handed to Ophis.

Having placed spectacles on his pencil thin nose Ophis read the letter, placed it in a pocket of his coat and as he did so, many miles away, the boat sailed away taking the King to safety.

With an expressionless face Ophis then prepared to greet the crowds outside.

The doors onto the balcony opened, and the new ruler of Kolokol stepped out, a stick thin hand waved at the people and for the first time the bells of the palace remained silent.

It was the first of many changes that people had not expected nor desired.

FOUR

Ophis takes charge

A S LUCK WOULD HAVE IT Ophis very soon grasped an opportunity. A sickness arrived in the land and everyone became very scared and were told to stay inside for safety.

Laws were passed and schools and businesses were closed, even churches. Many children were glad that they didn't have to go to lessons but soon missed their friends and their parents became more and more fearful.

One day the sickness went away and people were allowed out, but as they had for so long been apart, normal life took a long time to return. Then people discovered that while they were at home many of their freedoms had been taken away, and they were not given back. Ophis was in charge and to celebrate the ending of the sickness (which in the end people had not needed to fear) he had the name of the country changed to his own. Most bells never rang again.

Six years passed, six unhappy years. Times seems to pass more slowly when you are unhappy and for the people of the new land of Ophis each day seemed unending. *Beware of what you wish for* is a wise old saying because many thought that when the King went all the things they didn't like would get better. They found instead that all the things they had liked disappeared.

With each week came a change. As bells no longer rang in village after village people saw the lorries arrive and the bells taken away. There was soon, however, something to distract them. Shops sold less; food changed or wasn't available, but one of the biggest changes concerned truth itself.

One day people couldn't buy Kolokol Cake.
This was a lovely cake, full of sugar and fruit covered in cream. Chocolates wrapped in gold icing were placed around the edge. It was always eaten on special holidays like Easter and Whitsun.

One day the bakers stopped selling Kolokol Cake and then said it wasn't for sale ever again. Two years later, children in schools were taught that the Kolokol Cake was only ever eaten by the king. The very young could only imagine what it must have tasted like.

Sometimes when we don't have an answer to a problem it is easy to blame it on someone else. As the unhappy years passed everyone knew that Ophis was the problem, but they blamed each other rather than themselves. People who had come from other countries and were paid little to help care for the sick or very old were often criticised, and they would go to their small shared rooms after long days at work and wonder why so few were grateful or kind to them.

Most people got on with life, but deep down a secret hope remained that their young king would return.
If Ophis was the problem King John was an obvious solution.

The land that they had known only a few years' ago became in their minds even more happy and glorious, and many of those cheering when the King left conveniently said what a sad day it was!

At special dinners, guests would be asked to stand and lift into the air a drink (this is called a 'toast', something different to bread put in a toaster!).
"To President Ophis", people were supposed to say, but a few would whisper: "The King", as the drink was raised in the air and slowly passed over the water in a water glass.
The King, remember, lived far away across the Sea…
something Ophis never forgot as he would from time to time pat the letter from Nicolas in his breast pocket.

FIVE
Gabriel asks a question

THE SIXTH WINTER after the king's departure was colder than usual and Gabriel was in bed to keep warm. Mary, his mother, was sitting close by looking out of the window watching the snow settle on the window ledge.

She was telling him a story about the time he liked best, when he was young and there was still a king. His mother only ever smiled when she talked about the past, and so Gabriel knew that people had been happy then. But even when Mary smiled her eyes were sad, because the past had gone.

On that night she was talking about bells. They had rung on the day Gabriel was born, but only because he was born the same day as Prince John. When Ophis took over, life still for a while carried on. Parties were still held but because so many holidays and special occasions remembered the past they celebrated things that annoyed Ophis. The bells of Kolokol still rang on the days they always had. But slowly as the special days ended they were stopped.

Gabriel could not remember bells and he could only imagine their sound by what his mother told him. But he did know when they rang, because of nights like tonight when his mother talked to him. "Sometimes at times of great sadness a bell would ring slowly and sound as sad as sad could be. There was a time when during a war they were not rung because people knew if they heard them the enemy had arrived". She told him of the joyful sound the bells made on her wedding day when rose petals were thrown into the air and settled onto her veil. A year later Gabriel was born and the day the King sailed away someone else left too. As Mary turned to the window Gabriel could hear she was crying because that was the day she had last seen his father.

Pride in who we are

Gabriel, not knowing what to say, asked instead a question (something children are good at): "What does a bell sound like? "It is not like anything else in the world," she replied, Over the old cathedral were great bells, taller than a man, and they could be heard for miles around. Wherever you lived bells would ring and tell you the time or they would remind us of the day when heaven and earth met and an angel told a girl called Mary that she would help bring into the world the God who made everything. That's why we named you Gabriel".

"What does Gabriel mean?" asked Gabriel, "God is my strength", she replied, and returned to her story. "On Sundays we would hear the bells calling us to gather to celebrate all the gifts we have, and to remind us to share if we have more than we need. In the winter the horses and sleighs would have little silver bells on them so you could hear them even if you couldn't see them. But mostly we took them for granted. When you think something will last for ever you can stop taking any notice of it until it isn't there any more".
"Then when Ophis took over from the last of the kings we were told that bells couldn't ring because they were the sound of the past, and the sound of the things we shouldn't believe in any more.

Sometimes a brave priest would ring a bell but then one day the bells were taken away. We were told as well not to tell our children about them. Remember that the memory of the past can be controlled. When the past become a foreign country to the young we can do things differently, and not always for the best. Come to know about the past as it was, not as some think you should see it. The past offers us many questions, how we answer them shapes the future.

The greatest change however came when we realised that goodness and kindness don't just happen, and when people forget why they should be good, they can stop bothering"

SIX
Responding to a challenge

FOR WEEKS AFTERWARDS Gabriel thought about his name and where he could find courage: from his mother; the memory of his father; his love of his family; and the stories of what Kolokol had once been. He decided that before he slept he would kneel down by his bed and say his prayers. Then he would discover if someone listened.

One day he thought why should I be strong? He was walking to school when a sleigh passed him. Everyone knows what a sleigh looks like because Father Christmas rides in one and his sleigh can fly. But Gabriel couldn't hear the sleigh because it didn't have any bells on it. As he stepped back and stood between two young pine trees he noticed at the back of the sleigh little bits of leather that once were tied to their silver bells.

He then knew why he should be strong and live up to his name. The sound of bells came from a time when people were not sad. He would find a bell and discover for himself its sound.

The search begins

Gabriel had learnt that when you know why you must do something, and know what you must do, you have to work out how you achieve it. He knew the first step was to trust someone, and embark on a common endeavour.

School had been as boring as usual. All the books in school had on their cover a photo of Ophis Kirtle and his teachers often said that Ophis watched over them. Gabriel had discovered however one of his father's old books which was written before Ophis decided what version of the past could be taught. In school his teachers told his class that Kings and Bishops were rich, and ate too much, and took money from the poor to make bells because the Church – which was as bad as the King – only cared about money.

But in his father's book Edmund, King John's father, was called 'the Just' and Nicolas, the great Bishop of Myra, was shown giving gifts to the poor.

His father's book said that Nicolas gave gifts because, like millions of others, he followed someone who said the greatest thing we can do is love. Gabriel decided that to be strong he needed to read more and trust not what he was told but why and by whom.

To find a bell he needed as well to discover something important. He couldn't do it alone. He needed to trust someone, his sister.

A common endeavour

Georgiana was a little younger than Gabriel and although they sometimes fought and argued they had a bond that only a brother and sister can have.

Georgiana liked her name, but in the family her nickname was George. They were walking one morning to look for wood for the fire when Gabriel asked: "What do you think a bell looks like? George replied, "We don't know what a bell looks or sounds like, but our father wrote a book when he was teaching at the university about how we should think". Their father was called Peter and he had taught a subject called Philosophy.

George and Gabriel stopped for a moment because they had entered the King's Wood, and close by four roads met next to where "The Old Plough" stood. The Plough had been closed during the sickness and never re-opened and it was planned to go under a new road Ophis was planning to unite the north and south of the land. The more old houses that went under it the better, according to Ophis!

As they sat down on the trunk of an old elm, George continued: "I remember in Daddy's book he wrote about the questions that make people think. One is, 'If a tree falls in a wood and no one is there to listen, does it make a noise?' He also said that some of the most difficult questions can be answered by knowing what people in the past had written, and to trust them. Long ago someone said that everything we see has been made and when we think back millions and millions of years who made the first thing? Who started it?"

These were the questions that Ophis didn't want asked anymore which is why they closed the university and they didn't know where their father was. So George said: "Think"! "We know what things look and sound like, so when we find something we have never seen before and sound like something we have never heard before the chances are it will be a bell".

As George spoke she thought of how proud her father would be of her. They moved through the King's Wood to a larger wood called Honey Pot Hill. The lake in the middle of the wood appeared black. Snow had covered all the fields like a sheet and on the brittle branches of trees sat robins.

"Always winter and never Christmas", said Gabriel to himself as he thrust his hands deeper into his pockets to keep warm.

A bell is found

The bag they were carrying was nearly full of twigs they had picked from the ground. Gabriel was thinking of the day when the sleigh had passed him with the bits of leather that once had been tied to it. One of the bells must have fallen off and be buried under the snow, perhaps with a bit of leather still tied to it? He and George had found old coins whilst collecting wood and could work out their age by the image of a king or queen.

Ahead, soot black, lay a lake surrounded by leafless trees and suddenly they heard singing. The song came from the woods, where they could see a little column of smoke rising into the grey sky, and the song went:

Ring in the valiant man and free,
The larger heart, the kindlier hand.

They stopped. Then George saw a flash of ruby red in the sky. As she pointed to Gabriel to look at the robin landing in a branch, he looked to his left and noticed something glisten in the dappled light of the wood. He took George's hand and they walked to the source of this mysterious thing.

Let freedom ring

Under the branches of a great Hornbeam, behind an ancient Yew, its branches heavy with snow, something shone.

Reaching down Gabriel picked it up and inside the silver shell was snow and flecks of brown earth. Holding it up to the light George, with her little finger, picked out the frozen ice and felt something inside. They could see a chain with a small ball, made of metal, at its end.

"I think" said George, "this is a bell". "There is only one way to find out", said Gabriel and they shook it.

In the wood the silence was broken by a sound they had never heard: a ringing sound came from what they now knew must be a bell. A pure, joyful, ringing noise echoed around them, and the robins stilled and listened.

They rang the bell together and when silence embraced the wood again they heard someone laughing. Through the yews walked a man. As he got closer Gabriel and George saw

in his face something they saw in each other and he said,
"I have waited a long time to meet you".
They both knew it was their father, Peter.

With family again

Six years is a long time to talk about and after a long talk, and
a long walk, Peter said, "The day has come for me to return
home. Because you have found and rang a bell much will
happen, and happen very quickly".

As the tired sun went to sleep and they returned to Myra
they saw a very early snowdrop. Pointing to it Peter said:
"Snowdrops were once called 'Candlemas Bells' because they

would peep through the earth when we remembered, not long after Christmas, that the child born for us grew up, like I see you have grown".

Looking down at the white bell shaped flower their father continued, "Names matter. Your names, my name, the names of almost everything have meaning. Mary is a great name, as is Peter and George. Learn about a name and you will learn much. Soon we will see John and Nicolas again and the wonderful name of Kolokol will be restored".

Christmas is restored

After Gabriel, Georgiana and Peter had reached home Mary and Peter, after years of distancing, embraced. They talked for some time together. Then sitting in front of the fire the two children fed the flames with the twigs they had collected from their walk.

Their father then told them why he knew of Nicolas' promise. When the King and Nicolas, Princess Frederika and Rigsby the cat had left the palace they had stopped on the way to the mountains at the home of a close friend of the bishop.

"They stayed the night here", said Peter. "You don't remember but for that night three young children slept together, you and the King. Nicolas had with him three small

bags of money and two were left here for you. I knew that by their staying here and my being asked to take a letter to the Palace your mother would need money.

I saw Nicolas write the letter and so I became a part in the secret of the promise. After I had delivered the letter I knew Ophis Kirtle would have little time for universities, and so I decided to live in the woods close to home. I often saw you and your mother.

Although I didn't go far it was safer for you that you didn't know where I was. Sometimes the best thing we can do for others is the hardest thing we do to ourselves".

They then waited.

SEVEN
Better days return

IT WAS, at least in the old days, Christmas Eve.
Ophis was sitting in the King's study sipping water when he turned his face to the ceiling. A vibration and thumping sound shook the room. Cheers and shouts soon followed, both inside and outside the Palace.

Although it took some time for Ophis to realise what the noise was his long green clad legs soon got him to his elongated feet. Then he realised that the great bells, high up in the highest tower, were ringing.

Cautiously Ophis edged his way to the door. Upon opening it he could see people running around and one of the old servants had taken a royal standard from a cupboard (standard is the proper name of a flag with someone's shield on it). It was last flown the day before Ophis took power.

"Stop", screeched Ophis, his wrinkly neck tightening, and as he signalled for help he noticed the guards hadn't changed, but disappeared.

The good and faithful servant carried the folded standard to the door that opened onto the flag staff roof. He paused and he and Ophis for a second stared into each others eyes. Ophis noticed a look, a strange look of knowledge on the man's face. It was an expression that said, "I am not afraid of you any more".

As the bells rang and the King's standard was raised over the palace, Ophis, with power and strength draining from him sat down. His paper thin fingers reached into his coat pocket and felt the letter he had always kept with him. Nicolas and the King were coming back.

As the bells rang crowds gathered outside the palace. They saw the standard raised and the weary feeling of fear began to be replaced by a sense of hope and happiness.

The old flag pointed to what they knew must now happen, like Advent once pointed to the return of someone they could now speak of again. The crowd then began to sing a variation of an old Kolokol folk song, and louder and louder the people sang as they remembered what it was to be happy and free.

> *Ring out the old, ring in the new,*
> *Ring, happy bells, across the snow:*
> *Ophis is going, let him go;*
> *Ring out the false, ring in the true.*
>
> *Ring in the valiant man and free,*
> *The larger heart, the kindlier hand;*
> *Ring out the darkness of the land,*
> *Ring in the Christ that is to be.*

The eruption of song was soon commingled with the ringing of a more delicate noise. A sleigh appeared, its small bells ringing, and entered the Square. King John, now aged eight was seated, wearing the crown that was too big for him when he had left.

In the sleigh, drawn by four white horses (white horses are known as greys) sat Bishop Nicolas and Princess Frederika (holding an older and even fatter Rigsby). How many, thought the King, who were cheering him now had cheered when he left. Perhaps he thought, like him, they had grown and changed and learnt a great deal since then.

At the back of the sleigh were Peter, Mary, Gabriel and Georgiana.

From the palace, two soldiers, wearing again the uniforms from the days of the Kings, brought out Ophis. John stepped from the sleigh and the two met. "You have grown", the taller of the two said as the soldiers held his thin arms.

"I have thought a great deal about what we would do with you", said the King looking up to eyes that expressed little emotion. "A room in a prison, a job in the palace kitchen? One of my first decisions will be a sign of how things have changed, so I shall show what you should have learnt when you were young: mercy and forgiveness. But you must let those things enter what is left of your heart. There is a small island where you will be sent to. It has many fields where you can grow carrots and there is plenty of fresh water to drink, and I am told that at sunset the sea looks almost green. I hope there you might find happiness".

Ophis was taken to his little island (Fernandes Island it is called and if you are ever sailing past Kolokol it lies to the south, and you know if you are close because the carrots make the land look orange). As the years passed, and he worked on his harvests, he lived, as much as he could, happily ever after...

Pride in the future

As Ophis was led away, the King jumped back onto the sleigh and as loudly as he could shouted to the crowds, "My first words to you are not my own. Many years' ago my grandmother spoke at a difficult time when few people knew what to say and many were scared, the pride in who we are is not a part of our past, it defines our future. To the future, and to the cathedral!"

The thousands of people who had now surrounded him, followed the Sleigh as it slowly made its way through those who lined the streets waving.

From behind windows children were held up to see for the first time a king and to hear the sound of the bells, however difficult owing to the cheers and shouts.

As the procession turned into Franklin Square a coach, with four horses, waited. Everyone called the coach a carriage, but I'm sure you can imagine what it looked like. It had leather seats and four great wheels and the red paint was shiny and clean. The horses were brushed so they shined too and on them glistened brass and more bells.

As the sleigh stopped one of the old grooms came forward and took John's hand. "I drove your Father to his Coronation many years ago, and I drove Your Majesty to yours. Let me drive you now to where you belong".

So everyone moved from sleigh to coach and the procession continued. They arrived at the cathedral, closed for so long, and the King led everyone to the great door as it was slowly opened. They could see down the long passage under the great oak roof six covered shapes (this part of the church is called a nave because if you turned it upside down it looks like a ship, and lots of ships together make a navy!).

The cheering had stopped as the cool still air of the church embraced the King and his people, "The winter is gone and the time of singing has come", said John as he broke the silence, "Kolokol is restored. Tonight Christmas begins again, and Bishop Nicolas has sent the gifts he promised".

"Before you are six gifts: Bells, and on each bell is a name. Each name will be remembered. They are the names of those who made a new future possible by restoring what this land had once been:
    Mary, Peter, Gabriel, George, Nicolas,
    and last of all my name.
Today we begin a new journey, building on all that was good and all that we had taken for granted. When you hear them ring be thankful that you are free, and free to believe, to pray and hope and love. Better days have returned".

Nicolas returns with gifts

Then Nicholas returned. He entered his cathedral with two assistants (it is named after St Mary and All Souls, but everyone called it the cathedral).

One priest, who was called Fr Thomas (who had a wonderful beard and looked like a king himself) carried a small silver container, and as Nicolas signalled for everyone to kneel, the priest carried it to the King. John remained kneeling as the priest gently touched his head. Fr Thomas then walked with the silver container down the nave to where the gates were opened and, after walking up the steps to the High Altar, he placed it in a domed brass box, covered by a cloth.

As the priest closed the doors to the box a small bell rang, a light was placed in a silver hanging lamp (shaped like a boat). Then everyone stood up.

"You are not the only one who has come home", said the smiling bishop to the King as the cathedral felt alive again with a feeling of holiness. "You will know what I mean when you begin your First Communion classes".

John looked for a moment like the small boy he was. He may be King but like every 8 year old he had many classes to come, and much still to learn.

"Now unwrap the gifts I have brought", said the bishop, and as he spoke the covers were removed from the six bells. The second priest, who was called Fr Bradley, had once been an actor and with a flourish he took from his bag two containers, one containing water, and one containing oil.

"When our lives begin we are baptised, and these bells will have a long life too", said Fr Bradley as the bishop poured water onto the bells, calling each by name, and tracing a cross on each one.

Afterwards the bishop spoke in a language few understood but had been spoken in the cathedral for many hundreds of years. "Remember", said Georgiana to Gabriel, "if you don't understand something, learn about it. We should never stop learning".

Laudo Deum verum, plebem voco, festaque honoro

Gabriel, looked up to his father and said, "What did the bishop say to the bells when they can't hear anything?".
"*Laudo Deum verum, plebem voco, festaque honoro*, whispered Peter to his children, "the bells are being told their job! It means 'I praise the True God, call the people and honour the festivals'. The bells will soon speak, perhaps they can hear".

They were interrupted by the sound of the organ, and then by singing from the choir:

> *O holy night! The stars are brightly shining,*
> *It is the night of our dear Saviour's birth.*

As the music continued, Nicolas took from his finger the third and final gift. The ring that Nicolas had worn since the day they took the young King away was placed back on John's finger. The old bishop then placed his hands on the

King's shoulders and said, "You have become like a son to me and have grown to be kind and courageous. Wear this ring well." The Kingdom of Kolokol lived again.

When the sound of singing had faded away Nicholas turned to the people waiting, as they were for Midnight Mass to begin. As Christmas Eve would soon end and Christmas Day begin lots of things were happening at once. The crib was brought from the cellar and the bells were being drawn by ropes into the tower by John Taylor, the chief cathedral bell ringer.

Nicholas had now been dressed for Mass, and the priests were dressed with dalmatics (they could wear something else but that is for another story…). "Haven't we forgotten something?", said the King, as Nicolas took from his pocket his gloves. Shaylah, a young girl in the congregation, to her great grand-mother Curline, "We must keep up the standards". "Quite", Curline replied proudly.

Then Nicolas spoke:

"Many good things have been restored to this land tonight. The greatest gift of all is freedom.
Defend it and honour those who gave everything for it.
Freedom is not given, but achieved.
Great men and women of the past have known courage and the power of faith to overcome hatred.
Make their words and stories your own:

This is your hour
work together,
pray together,
struggle together,
stand up for freedom together,
let freedom ring."

Nicolas said again even more loudly, "Let freedom ring".

As he did so the new bells rang out from the cathedral tower for the first time, and Christmas began again.

Afterword

IF YOU ONE DAY VISIT St John's Church, Kensal Green you will first enter a gate close to a large lawn. It once formed part of a field owned long ago by an Archbishop who helped make St George the patron saint of England. Henry Chichele is also one of the founders of the College of All the Faithful Departed, Oxford, to which he also left his land, including this land in Kensal Green.

In 1844 the college donated this field for a church to be built, joined a little later by a school. The church was named after St John, the Gospel writer, because people knew that London was growing and they would need to hear the good news about Jesus (Gospel means good news). By this field, now with its church, was a green. This was a larger field and it was once known as the King's Wood. Although soon new houses covered the green, St John's, Kensal Green remains the name of the church today.

A Priest and a Football Club

The first priest at St Johns was called the Reverend Arthur Gore-Pemberton. When the church opened, one bell, (made by the same company who made 'Big Ben' for the Houses of Parliament) was put in the tower. The people of Kensal Green hoped for more bells, but sometimes other plans come along and Fr Arthur saw built around the church many houses, which became known as Queen's Park. This new estate meant that 8000 more people would be moving to his parish, and they would need things to do, and especially things for children to do. To the north of his parish, on land owned by All Souls College, the College Park Estate was built, and the people there had no priest or church. Fr Arthur therefore started a mission church, and one of his assistants became its first priest. It was here that a boys' club was formed, from which a football club emerged in 1882. It was Arthur Gore-Pemberton who allowed the boys to use the name of the mission as part of the new football club's title – Christ Church Rangers. In 1885 this club merged with another local club and became Queen's Park Rangers Football Club, a club which went on to be quite famous!

The one bell of 1844 rang out for many years as the world changed, and rang through different reigns, wars, and as London grew and grew. Then a special anniversary came along…

In 2019 St John's Church began the year by remembering that its grounds were once a field, given as a gift, and so donated £1000 to a local sport and community charity which works with children. The church also remembered that the old bell of 1844 had rung for a long time and that, for 175 years, people had wanted more bells. It was therefore decided to raise money for six new ones, and the church wrote to the owner of Queen's Park Football Club, Tony Fernandes asking if he might like to make a donation. He was reminded that it was Gore-Pemberton who had helped to start the team. Tony replied: he would pay for them all! After Tony visited the church the old bell retired and, on Christmas Day, they rang for the first time. They 'rang in' 2020 and we looked forward to their ringing for the first time ever on Easter Day. They did, but by then the church doors were closed.

A Play

Just before Christmas 2019 a children's play took place in church, when the six bells had not yet been carried up the tower. This book is the story that inspired the play. The characters are named after the saints to whom the bells are dedicated: St Mary, St John, the Archangel Gabriel, St George, St Peter, and St Nicolas. The story is based on what happened to bells in Russia during the years of Communism, and its themes include losing what we can take for granted, freedom, and being free to believe. It is also story about important teachings of Christianity and all faiths: that with faith comes hope and love; that being good and generous brings rewards in ways which we may never know.

For all the Saints

This story takes example from those who served Christ as their king, the saints. Saints were not perfect people, and they made mistakes, as we all do. Some did horrible things and then changed; many are called martyrs, because they saw their lives as less important than following the truth.

They are saints, however, because there is something in their lives which make them examples to us. They may have lived hundreds of years ago, but we can still try to be like them. The Church, quite simply, says that here are the people who are in heaven and are a good example as we try and follow the Lord, as they did heroically.

A New Year

At the beginning of 2020 St John's began the year with a second donation of £1000, this time to Aid to the Church in Need. After so many donations to us, we decided to help a church in Iraq. This church had been damaged and, as people returned to their village, they saw that their own bell tower and community centre needed rebuilding. We in Kensal Green then looked forward to Easter, and the seventy-five years of peace celebrations, marking the end of the Second World War. It was during this war that our own church was bombed.

We had planned to have a big party to celebrate freedom, and we wanted to include the many freedoms that matter, like not being treated differently because of our colour or background or what we believe. Bells were planned to ring all over the country, because in May 1945 victory was celebrated by the sound of church bells. The Rev Martin Luther King, in a famous speech, spoke about freedom ringing:

> "...when we allow freedom to ring, when we let it ring from every village and every hamlet, from every state and every city, we will be able to speed up that day when all of God's children, black men and white men, Jews and Gentiles, Protestants and Catholics, will be able to join hands and sing in the words of the old ... spiritual, "Free at last! free at last! Thank God Almighty, we are free at last!"

Then, in March 2020, the church was temporarily closed, owing to the nationwide lockdown caused by the Coronavirus pandemic.

Like so many schools, and shops, and businesses, all over Europe, the churches closed. People were asked to stay at home. But the bells at St Johns kept ringing. Every day in the evening they rang, and people listened. They became a sound of hope, and a sign of freedom. The two boys who played the young and older King, played in the church garden during this time: free to play at a time of great worry for so many.

This story was then changed slightly, but not its ending. We can take things for granted until they are not there anymore (like our freedoms); we can forget that many people in our world are not free; we can forget the poor, and those who no one listens to. The work of Aid to the Church in Need supports those who follow the Lord at great danger to themselves. When you hear the bells, says St Nicolas, stand up for freedom together. This is something that goes to the heart of the work of Aid to the Church in Need, to which all profits of sales of this book are will be donated. Finally, Helena and I are grateful to Nick Snode for his hard work in preparing this book for publication, and to the Very Reverend David Connor, Dean of Windsor, for his touching and powerful foreword.

Fr David Ackerman

The bells are blessed on St Nicholas Day 2019, they rang for the first time on Christmas Day.

The young King John and the older King John at the children's pageant, December 2019. During the pandemic of 2020 Dubem and Jidenna played in the Vicarage garden.

David and Emma on the beach at Selsey in April. They took Dubem and Jidenna, with their mother Anne-Francis for a day out. It was the first time Jidenna had seen the sea.

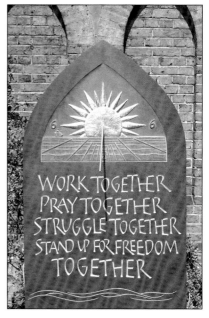

Fr David visiting staff in his local corner shop and the sundial, installed on 8th May, 2020, the 75th anniversary of VE Day.

That Rings a Bell...

**A short afterthought by Neville Kyrke-Smith,
National Director of Aid to the Church in Need UK**

THAT RINGS A BELL, I thought, when I read this story. I was thinking of my visits to Eastern Europe, to China and parts of the Middle East over the last thirty-five years. Often I have 'heard' the silence... witnessing attempts to silence the Faith by stopping the bells, as churches were closed, destroyed or blown up. This was done by the enemies of Christianity to prevent the proclamation of hope, and to stop the joy of God's love for all being rung out.

In 1999 I was in Minsk in Belarus, on the edge of Russia. I met the elderly and holy Cardinal Swiatek there, in a tiny upper study/bedroom at the Cathedral; he had been condemned to death in World War II by both the Germans and the Russians and spent ten years in the Gulag prison camps.

The restored Cathedral of the Holy Name of Mary is a beautiful building in Minsk. During Communist times the crypt was used as a shooting gallery and the main body – the nave – of the Cathedral was used as a sports hall and theatre. Aid to the Church in Need helped completely repair the floor, as well as many other projects, but it was the bells in particular I was thinking about.

For just near the Cathedral I saw the huge secret service headquarters of the KGB, where the bells from the Cathedral still hang in the tower of the building. The original huge bells were dragged down from the cathedral as the towers were blown up in 1951; these huge old bells were used by the communists on their 'feast days' – as a sign of the death of religion and of the triumph of the Workers Revolution. The KGB still keep the bells today – but now new church bells ring out in the rebuilt towers and Christ's hope is proclaimed once more, even amidst all the difficulties and challenges of life.

I joined the congregation in the Cathedral at Mass; it was a weekday, but there must have been over 300 people at Mass, half of whom were under twenty-five years old. Some trendy young men, with pony-tails, were there. Smartly dressed young girls in their late teens and early twenties were there. A nun in full habit prayed amongst them. Young children prayed with grandmothers. This was just a feria, no special feast day, but there could have been no better witness to a Church coming alive, rising from the ashes of atheism. A wonderful Mass, with full singing from the congregation, was celebrated. Then the bells rang out. The sound of freedom.

* * *

About the illustrator

Helena Tarrant trained in Graphic Design at the London College of Printing and has a BA degree in History of Art and English from the University of Hull.

After developing a career as an art consultant in the 1990s, Helena worked in a variety of part time roles to bring up her son. Having produced drawings all her life, she began at this time to develop her artistic work and her illustrations appeared in corporate magazines and executive workbooks.

Originally from Twickenham, Helena lived for 20 years in Maida Vale before returning to Twickenham where she now lives with her son.

Helena is a director of a business psychology company, for which she produces cartoons. She continues to expand her creative projects. Recently her work has appeared in workshops for the NHS, and she contributes regularly to the national bell-ringers' magazine *The Ringing World*. In early 2020 she finished writing and illustrating her first book.

Helena is a keen bell-ringer and rings at St Mary's Twickenham, where she learned campanology as a teenager. She is delighted to be involved with this truly inspiring and exciting book and its connection to the new bells at St John's Kensal Green. Her email is: helena.cartoonist@gmail.com